This edition published by Parragon Books Ltd in 2016

Parragon Books Ltd
Chartist House
15–17 Trim Street
Bath BA1 1HA, UK
www.parragon.com

ISBN 978-1-4748-5114-5

Printed in China

In today's hectic world, life moves pretty fast and it's tricky to find time to chill out. Sometimes it can seem like you have to become a super hero just to keep up with everything that needs to be done each day!

But we should try to take some time out on a regular basis, and what better way to escape the real world than with a DC Super Heroes colouring book? It ticks all the right boxes, with the added bonus of producing something awesome in the process.

There's no special skill or equipment required; just choose a page featuring your favourite DC Super Heroes and begin bringing the characters to life with colour.

Just as the DC Super Heroes have skills ready to be revealed when the time is right, we all have an inner artist waiting to be set free. And like Superman, Batman and The Flash, there are no limits to what you can achieve!

So it's time to aim high, be strong and use your laser vision to complete each page of *Comic Art Colouring.* And most of all ... have fun!

No. 38

Detective COMICS™

10¢